A Deans Tall Story Book

Daisy the Naughty Kitten

A Deans Tall Story Book

Daisy the Naughty Kitten

Illustrated by Douglas Hall

Daisy was a spoilt kitten, and she was sometimes rather naughty. The trouble was that Daisy was jealous of her older sister Violet's dolly.

When it was time for Violet to take Dolly for a walk, Daisy would climb into the doll's pram. When she was taken out to make room for Dolly, Daisy was not pleased.

At teatime, Violet would not let Daisy join in her tea-party.

Daisy always wanted to sit at the table and drink from the tea-set, just as Dolly did.

One day a friend came to visit Violet. The friends played with their dolls all afternoon, which made Daisy very annoyed. "They should play with *me*," she thought. "I will *make* them take notice of *me*."

So Daisy climbed to the top
of a tree and pretended
she could not get down.
Mummy and Daddy and Violet
were worried. They fussed
and shouted and looked
anxiously up at Daisy
in the tree.
Daisy *was* pleased.

Daisy stayed up the tree all night and everyone stayed awake to coax her down. She felt very important.

Next day, Daddy called at the fire station to ask for help. The fireman came to the tree with a long ladder, but even he could not catch naughty Daisy.

Then Violet, who was clever, took the doll's pram and the tea-set into the garden.

"Come down from the tree," she called to Daisy,

"and I will
give you a
ride in the
pram and you can
drink from the tea-set."
At once Daisy scrambled
down the tree.
"Daisy is a naughty kitten,"
said the fireman,
"but Violet is clever."

First published in 1985 by
Deans International Publishing
52–54 Southwark Street, London SE1 1UA
A division of The Hamlyn Publishing Group Limited
London · New York · Sydney · Toronto

ISBN 0 603 00421 0

Filmset in Futura by Filmtype Services Limited,
Scarborough, North Yorkshire.

Printed and Bound by Purnell and Sons (Book Production) Ltd.,
Paulton,
Bristol.
Member of BPCC plc